Dinosaur Detective

Contents

Dinosaur Detective

Written by Harlene Baker
Illustrated by Geoffrey Cox

You can find out about dinosaurs
by looking at their fossils.
I found out how fossils were made
before I went on a fossil-finding trip.

How is a dinosaur fossil made?

1 A dinosaur died and fell into the mud.
Parts of the dinosaur rotted away.
The dinosaur bones did not rot away.

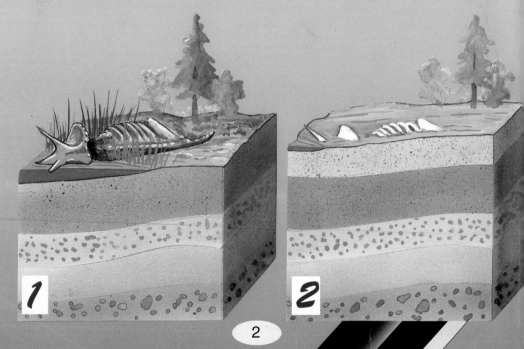

2 Sand and dirt went on top
of the bones.

3 Many, many years later,
the sand and dirt
turned into rock.
The dinosaur's bones were in the rock.
The dinosaur's bones were now fossils.

4 The rocks were pushed up
to the top of the land.
Fossil finders found the fossils.
They looked at the fossils
to find out how dinosaurs lived.

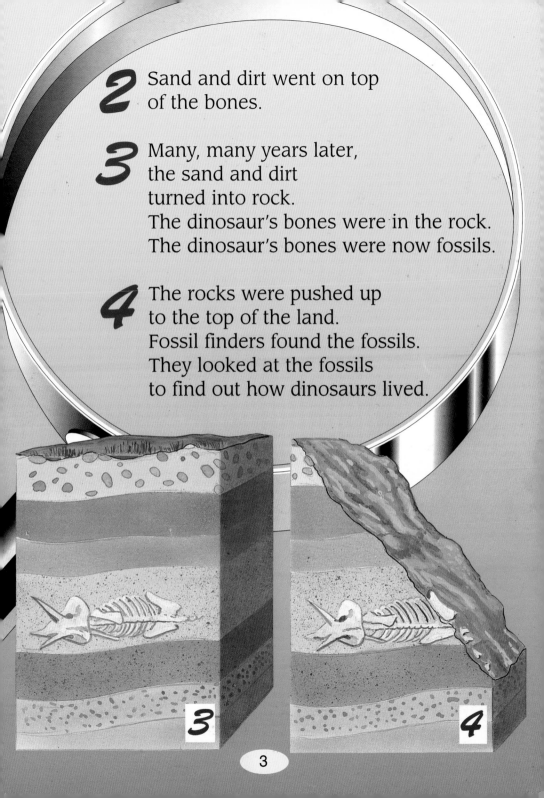

What you will need for a fossil hunt

A hard hat:
to keep your head safe

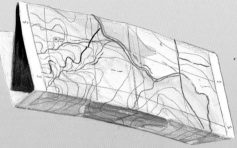

A map: to find out how
to get to the fossils

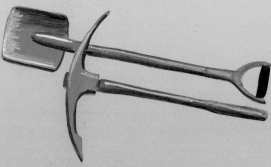

A pick and shovel:
to get the big rocks
away from the fossil

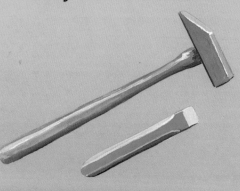

A chisel and hammer:
to get the small rocks
away from the fossil

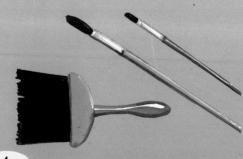

Brushes:
to brush away bits of
sand or stone

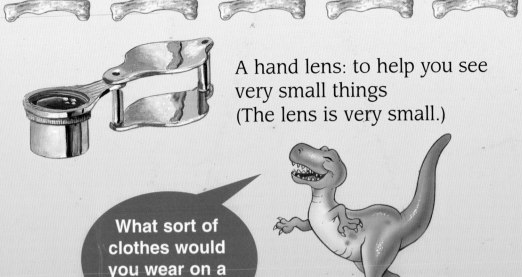

A hand lens: to help you see very small things
(The lens is very small.)

What sort of clothes would you wear on a fossil hunt?

My fossil-finding trip

First of all we looked on our map.
We looked for a place
where some fossils had been found.
We wanted to find fossils there, too!

What to look for

We looked for fossil bones
sticking out of the hills.
We saw little bits of sandstone
and little bits of white bone.
We found a fossil bone
and we were going to dig it out!

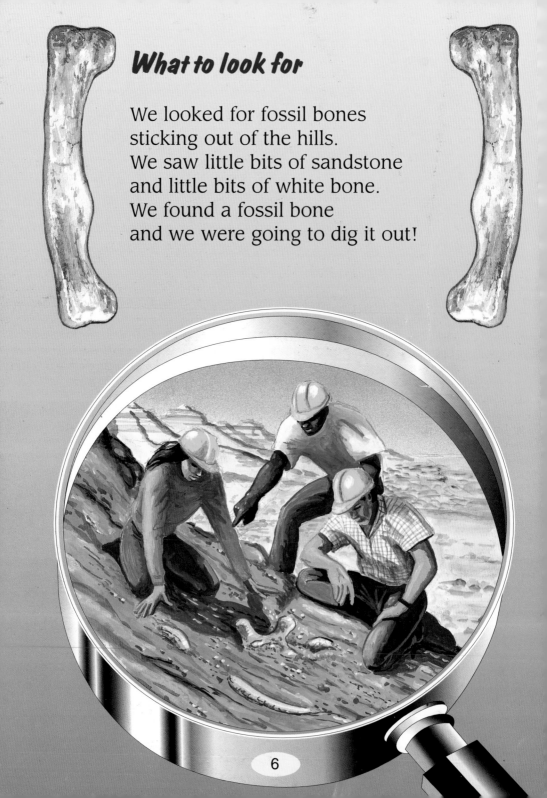

Getting the fossils out

We used a chisel
and a hammer
to get the rocks
away from the fossil.

We didn't dig close
to the fossil.
We didn't want to break
the fossil.
We moved the little rocks
away from the fossil
with our hands
or with little brushes.

We took a photo
of the fossil
before it was taken away.
The photo showed people
where the fossil was found.

Getting more fossils out

Some fossils
are in big rocks.
So we have to take
parts of the big rock away.
Then we can start
to take the fossil
out of the rock.

If the fossil is in clay,
we have to take the clay away
with our hands.
Then we put wet paper
and plaster on the fossil.

Now the fossil will not break.

Plaster?
How does that
work?

After the fossil hunt

We took the dinosaur fossil
to people who knew about fossils.
First, they took away the wet paper
and plaster from the fossil.
Then they cut away the rock.
They told us many things about the dinosaur
after they had looked at our fossil.

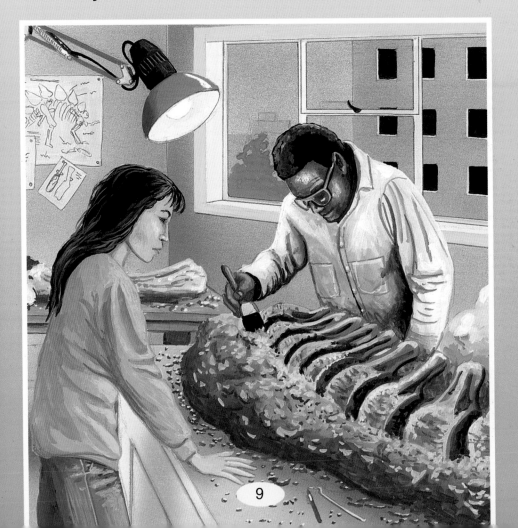

9

Myths and Truths

Written by Jacob Green   Illustrated by Geoffrey Cox

There are many myths about dinosaurs.
Myths are stories
that many people think are true.
Now fossil finders have found out
that some of these myths are not true.

What Were Dinosaurs?
Myth –
Dinosaurs were lizards.
People who found
the first dinosaur fossils
did not know what they were.
They said the bones were
from a giant lizard.

Truth –
Dinosaurs were not lizards.
People now know
what dinosaur fossils are.
Fossil finders have found out
that there were more than 350 kinds of dinosaurs.
Fossil finders are still finding
new dinosaur fossils.

Myth –
Dinosaurs were dragons.
People said that dinosaur fossils
were dragon bones.
They put little bits of bone
in their food.
They said that the dragon bones
would help them if they were sick.

Truth –
Dinosaurs were not dragons.
Dinosaurs lived right here on Earth.
Now we look at dinosaur bones
to find out how dinosaurs lived.

What Did Dinosaurs Look Like?

Myth –
Some dinosaurs had legs like a crocodile.
Dinosaurs had legs on the side of their body.

Truth –
Dinosaurs did not have legs like a crocodile.
Dinosaurs had legs like a horse.
The dinosaur's legs were under its body,
so some dinosaurs could stand up and walk.

Horse

Crocodile

Write your own dinosaur myth.

What Were Dinosaurs Like?

Myth –
All dinosaurs were the same.
People said
that there were not many dinosaurs.
They did not know
that more dinosaur fossils
would be found.

Truth –
All dinosaurs were not the same.
There were many, many dinosaurs.
Some dinosaurs looked like lizards,
and some dinosaurs looked like birds.

Dinosaur Fossils

Myth –
Fossil finders can still find dinosaur skin on a fossil.
The skin is still on the dinosaur fossil.

Truth –
Fossil finders cannot find dinosaur skin on a fossil.
Dinosaur skin rots away.
It is dinosaur bones and teeth
that are fossils.
Some fossil finders
found the shape of dinosaur skin
in a rock.
The skin was not the real skin
of the dinosaur.

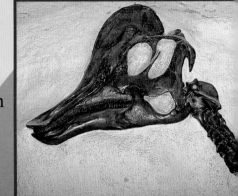

Dinosaur Babies

Myth –
Dinosaurs did not lay eggs.
Mother dinosaurs
had live baby dinosaurs.

Truth –
Dinosaurs did lay eggs.
Fossil finders have dug up
many dinosaur eggs.
Some of the eggs
had baby dinosaur bones
in them.

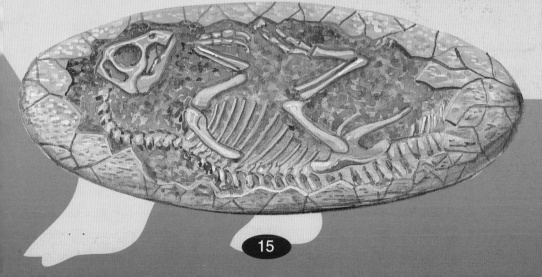

Myth –
Dinosaurs did not look after their babies.
Dinosaurs laid their eggs
and then went away.
They did not wait
for the baby dinosaurs
to come out of the eggs.

What other myths and truths do you know about dinosaurs?

Truth –
Some dinosaurs did look after their babies.
Fossil finders found some fossils
of dinosaur babies.
The dinosaur babies
were still in their nests.
They were fed in their nests.
The fossil finders
called this mother dinosaur
the Good Mother.
The Good Mother fed her babies
until they could get their own food.

THE TIME STONE

Written by Ann-Marie Heffernan   Illustrated by Marjorie Scott

Tom and Brad and Yasmin
were at the dinosaur park.
They were on a school trip.
A fossil finder was showing them
how to work on a fossil bone.
She had a small brush in her hand.
She was moving the sand
away from a dinosaur fossil.

"This is not fun! Let's go and look
for dinosaur eggs," said Tom.

Tom and Brad and Yasmin
went looking for dinosaur eggs.
Tom ran so fast that he fell down.
He fell over a stone.

"Hey, look at this stone," Tom said.
He picked up the stone.
A light was coming out of it.

"Let me hold it!" said Yasmin. "It's cool."

Their teacher came over to see
what Brad and Yasmin and Tom were doing.
"What's cool?" asked their teacher.

"Oh, just this dinosaur park," said Yasmin.
She hid the stone.

"Come on. We have to get on the bus, now,"
called the teacher.
"I hope you have made
a lot of notes for your homework."

Brad and Tom and Yasmin got on the bus.

"Come to my house after school," said Yasmin.
"Then we can all look at the stone."

When they got home,
Tom and Brad ran to Yasmin's house.
Yasmin showed them the stone.
Brad took it out of Yasmin's hand.

Then in a flash, Brad was gone.
He left Yasmin's house
and landed on Green Street.
Green Street was far away
from Yasmin's house.

"Oh no, the stone has taken me to Green Street.
I've got to go back and tell Tom and Yasmin
about the stone," said Brad.

Brad ran all the way back to Yasmin's house.
He told Tom and Yasmin where he had been.
He told Tom and Yasmin
that the stone had taken him
all the way to Green Street.

"All I had to do was to think of Green Street,"
said Brad. "And the stone took me there!"

"Wow, that stone is great," said Yasmin.
"Tom, you can go back to the dinosaur park.
Then you can make some notes
for our homework."

Tom had the stone in his hand.
He was thinking about the dinosaur park.

In a flash, the stone took him
to the dinosaur park.
Tom couldn't see the fossil bones,
but he could see lots of trees.

"Oh no, where is the dinosaur park?"
said Tom.

He saw some big footprints on the ground.
But then the ground began to shake.

Tom heard a loud roar.
The roar got louder and louder.
Tom looked to see what was roaring.
Tom saw a dinosaur!
It was a real dinosaur!
The dinosaur was looking at Tom.

Tom started to run.
He ran past the big footprints.
He ran past some nests.
In the nests were baby dinosaurs.

"Oh, no," said Tom.
"They are baby dinosaurs
and that big dinosaur must be their mother!"

Tom looked back to see where the dinosaur was.

The dinosaur was coming after Tom.
Tom could see the dinosaur's big head
and very big teeth.

"That dinosaur wants to eat me!
I have to get away," said Tom.

Then Tom looked at the stone in his hand.
He thought very, very hard.
He shut his eyes
and thought about Yasmin's house.
The stone started to work.
The stone took Tom away from the dinosaur park.
The stone took Tom back to Yasmin's house.

Yasmin and Brad were looking at him.
"Where have you been?" they asked.

Tom told them about the big dinosaur.
He told them that the dinosaur
wanted to eat him.

"Wow, but all dinosaurs are dead,"
said Brad.

"Well, I did see a dinosaur," said Tom.
"And the time stone took me there."

"The time stone is great," said Yasmin.
"Now we can do our school work on dinosaurs."

"Yes," said Brad. "The time stone
can tell us what is going to happen, too."

"We can see what is going to happen at school
and we can see who will get on
the football team," said Tom.

"Wow, what a great stone," said Yasmin.

Write another
adventure of the
time stone.

Making Dinosaurs Come to Life

Written by Ann-Marie Heffernan
Illustrated by Paul Rogers

Leroy Lewis
makes dinosaurs
come to life.
He draws dinosaurs
on his computer.
Then he makes
the dinosaurs move.
Leroy is making a dinosaur
for a movie.
He works in Los Angeles
in the United States.

Q Have you always liked to draw?

A Yes, I have always liked to draw. Then I found out that you could use a computer to draw. I liked drawing on the computer. Now I use the computer all the time. I make drawings that move. My drawings are used in movies.

A "Q" stands for question, and an "A" stands for answer.

Q Can you make dinosaurs
come to life in a movie?

A Yes,
I can make dinosaurs come to life
in a movie.
I'm working on a movie
with many dinosaurs in it.
One of the dinosaurs in the movie
is a T-Rex.
This is my first
dinosaur movie.

Which part of making dinosaurs do you think Leroy likes best?

Q How do you make dinosaurs
come to life in a movie?

A First, we look at a lot of drawings
and pictures of dinosaurs.
We also look at models of dinosaurs.
We read books about dinosaurs, too.
Then we look at how some animals move.
We look at big birds
because some dinosaurs moved like birds.

The Big, Big
Dinosaur
Book

We put all the drawings
and pictures of dinosaurs
into the computer.
Then we make a model
of the dinosaur on the computer.
We paint the dinosaur, too.
And then someone adds
the music and sound.
Then you can see my dinosaur
at the movies.

Write
some more
questions
that you
would like to
ask Leroy.

WILDCATS
Tiger

Glossary

- **chisel** – a tool with a sharp edge used for cutting

- **clay** – an earth used by potters to make pots and models

- **fossils** – the remains or prints of animals (or plants) that lived a long time ago

- **pick** – a tool with a pointed metal head used to break up rock or hard earth

- **plaster** – a mix of lime, sand, and water that makes a hard coating when dried

- **sandstone** – a kind of rock that is made from mostly sand

- **shovel** – a spadelike tool with a large scoop used for lifting and moving earth